Leave the flurry
To the masses;
Take your time
And shine your glasses.

VOICES

an anthology of poems and pictures

edited by GEOFFREY SUMMERFIELD

the fifth book

Rand McNally & Company · CHICAGO

Acknowledgements

For permission to reprint copyrighted material in this volume, grateful acknowledgement is made to the following:

Aldine Publishing Company: For "Chinese Cat," "French Persian Cats Having a Ball," "Orgy," "Pomander," "Strawberries," and "Summer Haiku," all reprinted from Edwin Morgan, *The Second Life* (Edinburgh: Edinburgh University Press, 1968); copyright © by Edwin Morgan and Edinburgh University Press.

Mr. William S. Burford and Southern Methodist University Press: For "A Christmas Tree" from *Man Now* by William Burford. Reprinted by permission of the author and Southern Methodist University Press.

Calder and Boyars Ltd.: For "Don't Sign Anything" from *Poems 1950-65* by Robert Creeley. For "The Performance" by James Dickey.

Chatto and Windus, Ltd.: For "Leader of Men" from *Surroundings* by Norman MacCaig. Reprinted by permission of Chatto and Windus Ltd.

Collins-Knowlton-Wing, Inc.: For "Cat-Goddesses" and "One Hard Look," both from *Collected Poems, 1955*, by Robert Graves. Published by Doubleday & Company, 1955. Copyright © 1955 by Robert Graves. Reprinted by permission of Collins-Knowlton-Wing, Inc.

Constable and Company Ltd.: For the translation of "The Red Cockatoo."

Doubleday & Company, Inc.: For "Lull" from *The Collected Poems of Theodore Roethke*. Copyright 1940 by Theodore Roethke. Reprinted by permission of Doubleday & Company, Inc.

Allan Dugan: For "On Hurricane Jackson" from *Poems* by Allan Dugan. First published by Yale University Press. Copyright by Allan Dugan. Reprinted by permission of the author.

Edinburgh University Press: For "Strawberries" by Edwin Morgan, from *Scottish Poetry Number One*.

Follett Publishing Company: For "Tribute to Henry Ford 1, 2, 3" by Richard Kostelanetz. Reprinted from *The Young American Poets*, edited by Paul Carroll, copyright © 1968, by Follett Publishing Company and used by their permission.

Donald Hall and Saturday Review, Inc.: For "Transcontinent" by Donald Hall. Copyright 1959 by the Saturday Review, Inc. From *The Saturday Review*, April 11, 1959.

Harcourt, Brace & World, Inc. For "a man who had fallen among thieves," "next to of course god america i," "a politician is an arse upon," and "since feeling is first," all from *Poems 1923-1954* by E. E. Cummings. Copyright 1954 by E. E. Cummings. For "Morning at the Window" and "Preludes I and II" from *The Complete*

(Acknowledgements continued on page 120)

Editorial Director: Joy Zweigler
Cover photograph by Dan Morrill

Contents

Extracts from "The People, Yes"

"Isn't that an iceberg on the horizon, Captain?"
"Yes, Madam."
"What if we get in a collision with it?"
"The iceberg, Madam, will move right along
    as though nothing had happened."

. . . .

A Scotsman keeps the Sabbath and anything else he can lay his
    hands on, say the English.
A fighting Frenchman runs away from even a she-goat, say the
    Germans.
A Russian, say the Poles, can be cheated only by a gypsy, a gypsy
    by a Jew, a Jew by a Greek, and a Greek by the devil.
"If I owned Texas and hell I would rent Texas and move to hell,"
    said a famous general.
"That's right," wrote a Texas editor. "Every man for his own
    country."
The Peloponnesians pulled these long ago, so did the Russians,
    the Chinese, even the Fijis with rings in their noses.
    Likewise:
An American is an Anglo-Saxon when an Englishman wants
    something from him: or:
When a Frenchman has drunk too much he wants to dance, a
    German to sing, a Spaniard to gamble, an Italian to brag, an
    Irishman to fight, an American to make a speech: or:
"What is dumber than a dumb Irishman?" "A smart Swede."
These are in all tongues and regions of men. Often they bring
    laughter and sometimes blood.
The propagandas of hate and war always monkey with the
    buzz-saw of race and nationality, breed and kin, seldom saying,
    "When in doubt hold your tongue."
In breathing spells of bloody combat between Christian nations
    the order goes out: "Don't let the men in the front-line
    trenches fraternize!"

. . . .

aw nuts aw go peddle yer papers
where did ja cop dat monkeyface
     jeez ja see dat skirt
     did ja glom dat moll
who was tellin you we wuz brudders
how come ya get on dis side deh street
go home and tell yer mudder she wants yuh
chase yer shadder aroun deh corner
yuh come to me wid a lot uh arkymalarky
     a bing in de bean fer you yeah
how come ya get on dis side deh street
go home and get yer umbreller washed
     den get yer face lifted
dis corner is mine — see — dis corner is mine
gwan ja tink ya gonna get dis f'm me fer nuttin
     nobody gets nuttin fer nuttin
      gwan monkeyface peddle yer papers
ya can't kiss yerself in here   dis is all fixed

. . . .

"How do you do, my farmer friend?"
"Howdy."

"Nice looking country you have here."
"Fer them that likes it."
"Live here all your life?"
"Not yit."

. . . .

"Yesterday," said the college boy home on vacation, "we autoed
    to the country club, golfed till dark, bridged a while, and
    autoed home."
"Yesterday," said the father, "I muled to the cornfield and
    gee-hawed till sundown, then I suppered till dark, piped till
    nine, bedsteaded till five, breakfasted and went muling again."

. . . .

Lawyer: What was the distance between the two towns?
Witness: Two miles as the cry flows.
Lawyer: You mean as the crow flies.
Judge: No, he means as the fly crows.

CARL SANDBURG

I, Too, Sing America

I, too, sing America.

I am the darker brother.
They send me to eat in the kitchen
When company comes,
But I laugh,
And eat well,
And grow strong.

Tomorrow,
I'll be at the table
When company comes.
Nobody'll dare
Say to me,
"Eat in the kitchen,"
Then.

Besides,
They'll see how beautiful I am
And be ashamed —

I, too, am America.

LANGSTON HUGHES

As Others See Us

With "No Admittance" printed on my heart,
  I go abroad, and play my public part;
And win applause — I have no cause to be
  Ashamed of that strange self that others see.

But how can I reveal to you, and you,
  My real self's hidden and unlovely hue?
How can I undeceive, how end despair
  Of this intolerable make-believe?

You must see with God's eyes, or I must wear
  My furtive failures stark upon my sleeve.

BASIL DOWLING

I Am

I am — yet what I am, none cares or knows;
  My friends forsake me like a memory lost:
I am the self-consumer of my woes —
  They rise and vanish in oblivions host,
Like shadows in love frenzied stifled throes
  And yet I am, and live — like vapours tost

Into the nothingness of scorn and noise,
  Into the living sea of waking dreams,
Where there is neither sense of life or joys,
  But the vast shipwreck of my life's esteems;
Even the dearest that I love the best
  Are strange — nay, rather, stranger than the rest.

I long for scenes where man hath never trod
  A place where woman never smiled or wept
There to abide with my Creator God,
  And sleep as I in childhood sweetly slept,
Untroubling and untroubled where I lie
  The grass below, above, the vaulted sky.

JOHN CLARE

Africa's Plea

I am not you —
but you will not
give me a chance,
will not let me be *me*.

"If I were you" —
but you know
I am not you,
yet you will not
let me be *me*.

You meddle, interfere
in my affairs
as if they were yours
and you were me.

You are unfair, unwise,
foolish to think
that I can be you,
talk, act
and think like you.

God made me *me*.
He made you *you*.
For God's sake
Let me be *me*.

ROLAND TOMBEKAI DEMPSTER

Telephone Conversation

The price seemed reasonable, location
Indifferent. The landlady swore she lived
Off premises. Nothing remained
But self-confession. "Madam," I warned,
"I hate a wasted journey — I am African."
Silence. Silenced transmission of
Pressurized good-breeding. Voice, when it came,
Lipstick coated, long gold-rolled
Cigarette-holder pipped. Caught I was, foully.
"HOW DARK?" . . . I had not misheard . . . "ARE YOU LIGHT
OR VERY DARK?" Button B. Button A. Stench
Of rancid breath of public hide-and-speak.
Red booth. Red pillar-box. Red double-tiered
Omnibus squelching tar. It *was* real! Shamed
By ill-mannered silence, surrender
Pushed dumbfoundment to beg simplification.
Considerate she was, varying the emphasis —
"ARE YOU DARK? OR VERY LIGHT?" Revelation came.
"You mean — like plain or milk chocolate?"
Her assent was clinical, crushing in its light
Impersonality. Rapidly, wave-length adjusted,
I chose. "West African sepia" — and as afterthought,
"Down in my passport." Silence for spectroscopic
Flight of fancy, till truthfulness clanged her accent
Hard on the mouthpiece. "WHAT'S THAT?" conceding
"DON'T KNOW WHAT THAT IS." "Like brunette."
"THAT'S DARK, ISN'T IT?" "Not altogether.
Facially, I am brunette, but, madam, you should see
The rest of me. Palm of my hand, soles of my feet
Are a peroxide blond. Friction, caused —
Foolishly, madam — by sitting down, has turned
My bottom raven black — One moment, madam!" — sensing
Her receiver rearing on the thunderclap
About my ears — "Madam," I pleaded, "wouldn't you rather
See for yourself?"

WOLE SOYINKA

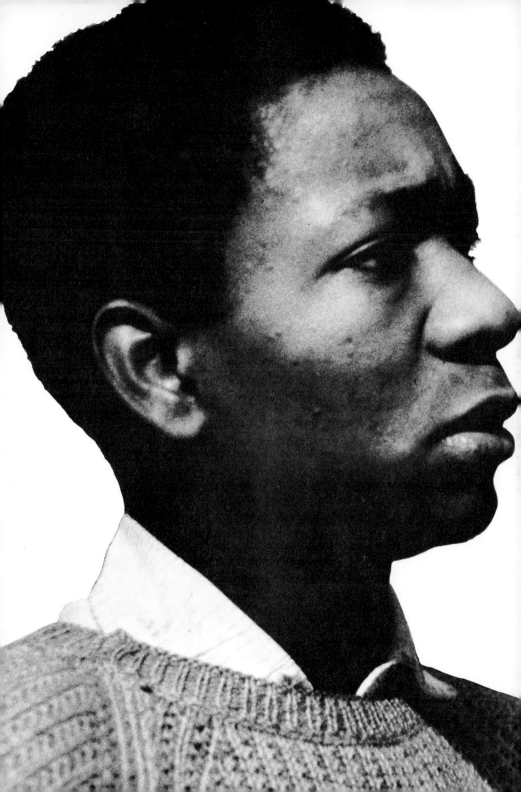

Each Morning
From "Hymn for Lanie Poo"

4

Each morning
I go down
to Gansevoort St.
and stand on the docks.
I stare out
at the horizon
until it gets up
and comes to embrace
me. I
make believe
it is my father.
This is known
as genealogy.

LEROI JONES

After Looking into a Book Belonging to My Great-Grandfather Eli Eliakim Plutzik

I am troubled by the blank fields, the speechless graves.
Since the names were carved upon wood, there is no word
For the thousand years that shaped this scribbling fist
And the eyes staring at strange places and times
Beyond the veldt dragging to Poland.
Lovers of words make simple peace with death,
At last demanding, to close the door to the cold,
Only *Here lies someone.*
Here lie no one and no one, your fathers and mothers.

HYAM PLUTZIK

Ute Mountain

"When I am gone,"
the old chief said,
"if you need me, call me,"
and down he lay, became stone.

They were giants then
(as you may see),
and we
are not the shadows of such men.

The long splayed Indian hair
spread ravelling out
behind the rocky head
in groins, ravines;

petered across the desert plain
through Colorado,
transmitting force
in a single undulant unbroken line

from toe to hair-tip: there
profiled, inclined away from one
are features, foreshortened, and the high
blade of the cheekbone.

Reading it so, the eye
can take the entire great
straddle of mountain-mass,
passing down elbows, knees, and feet.

"If you need me, call me."
His singularity dominates the plain
as we call to our aid his image:
thus men make a mountain.

CHARLES TOMLINSON

Hay for the Horses

He had driven half the night
From far down San Joaquin
Through Mariposa, up the
Dangerous mountain roads,
And pulled in at eight a.m.
With his big truckload of hay behind the barn.
With winch and ropes and hooks
We stacked the bales up clean
To splintery redwood rafters
High in the dark, flecks of alfalfa
Whirling through shingle-cracks of light,
Itch of haydust in the sweaty shirt and shoes.
At lunchtime under Black oak
Out in the hot corral,
— The old mare nosing lunchpails,
Grasshoppers crackling in the weeds —
"I'm sixty-eight," he said,
"I first bucked hay when I was seventeen.
I thought, that day I started,
I sure would hate to do this all my life.
And dammit, that's just what
I've gone and done."

GARY SNYDER

Desiring To Give All

Desiring to give all, to be all gift,
A living giver, then a giver dead,
He gave to friends the liveliness of his head,
Then stretching generosity with thrift,
Pondered if head itself, the clean bare skull,
Might not be saved and deeded to a friend
So that memorial and functional
Might thrive and blend
In an undying fate
As doorstop or as paper-weight.

ROBERT FRANCIS

Locked In

All my life I lived in a cocoanut.
It was cramped and dark.
Especially in the morning when I had to shave.
But what pained me most was that I had no way
to get into touch with the outside world.
If no one out there happened to find the cocoanut,
if no one cracked it, then I was doomed
to live all my life in the nut, and maybe even die there.
I died in the cocoanut.
A couple of years later they found the cocoanut,
cracked it, and found me shrunk and crumpled inside.
"What an accident!"
"If only we had found it earlier . . ."
"Then maybe we could have saved him."
"Maybe there are more of them locked in like that . . ."
"Whom we might be able to save,"
they said, and started knocking to pieces every cocoanut
within reach.
No use! Meaningless! A waste of time!
A person who chooses to live in a cocoanut!
Such a nut is one in a million!
But I have a brother-in-law who
lives in an
acorn

INGEMAR GUSTAFSON Translated from the Swedish by May Swenson

Skinny Poem

Skinny
poem,
all
your
ribs
showing
even
without
a
deep
breath

thin
legs
rotted
with
disease.

Live
here!
on
this
page,
barely
making
it,
like

the
mass
of
mankind.

LOU LIPSITZ

Things in Common

We have a good relationship, the elevator boy and I.
I can always be cheerful with him.
We make jokes. We both belong to the TGIF Club.
No matter how artificial and stiff I've had to be in the office,
seems like I can be natural with *him*.
We have basic things in common —
the weather, baseball, hangovers,
the superiority of Friday over Monday.

It's true I make it a point to be pleasant to him. Why?
Honest, its because I really like him.
Individually, I mean.
There's something about him — relaxed and balanced
like a dancer or a cat —
as if he knows who he is and where he's at.
At least he knows how to act like that.
Wish I could say the same for myself.

I like his looks, his manner, his red shirt,
the smooth panther shape to his head and neck.
I like it that he knows I don't mean to flirt —
even though I really like him.
I feel he knows I know the score.
It's all in the gleam of his eyes,
the white of his teeth, when he slides back the door
and says, "TGIF, Ma'am, have a nice weekend."

He's strong muscled, good looking — could be 35 —
though with his cap off he's 50, I suppose.
So am I. Hope he thinks I look younger too.
I want him to like it that my eyes are blue —

I want him to really like me.
We look straight at each other when we say goodnight.
Is he thinking it's only an accident I'm white?
"TGIF," we say. "Have a nice weekend."

That's the way it's been so far.
We have a good relationship, just the two of us
and the little stool on which he never sits, in the car.
Fridays I work late. I'm the last one down.
Been, let's see, 11 years now . . .
These days I hug the newspaper to me so the headlines won't show.
Why he never has a paper I don't know.
Probably not supposed to read in the elevator.

Lately I've asked myself why don't I say:
"What do you think of the mess down South, Willie?
Or for that matter, right here in D.C.?"
Wish I dared ask him. Or that he'd find a way to put it to me.
I'd like to say bluntly, "Willie, will there be war?"
Neither of us has been able to say it so far.
Will I dare, someday? I doubt it . . . Not *me*, to *him*. . . .
"Thank God It's Friday," we say. "Have a nice weekend."

MAY SWENSON

Merritt Parkway

As if it were
forever that they move, that we
keep moving —

Under a wan sky where
as the lights went on a star
pierced the haze & now
follows steadily
a constant
above our six lanes
the dreamlike continuum . . .

And the people — ourselves!
  the humans from inside the
  cars, apparent
  only at gasoline stops
                unsure,
      eyeing each other

                    drink coffee hastily at the
                slot machines & hurry
          back to the cars
          vanish
          into them forever, to
          keep moving —

Houses now & then beyond the
sealed road, the trees/trees, bushes
passing by, passing
      the cars that
          keep moving ahead of
      us, past us, pressing behind us
                    and
              over left, those that come
        toward us shining too brightly
moving relentlessly

    in six lanes, gliding
north & south, speeding with
a slurred sound —

DENISE LEVERTOV

Mousemeal

My son invites me to witness with him
a children's program, a series of cartoons,
on television. Addressing myself to share
his harmless pleasures, I am horrified
by the unbridled violence and hostility
of the imagined world he takes in stride,
where human beings dressed in the skins of mice
are eaten by portcullises and cowcatchers,
digested through the winding corridors
of organs, overshoes, boa constrictors
and locomotive boilers, to be excreted
in waters where shark and squid and abalone
wait to employ their tentacles and jaws.
It seems there is no object in this world
unable to become a gullet with great lonely teeth;
sometimes a set of teeth all by itself
comes clacking over an endless plain
after the moving mouse; and though the mouse
wins in the end, the tail of one cartoon
is spliced into the mouth of the next, where his
rapid and trivial agony repeats itself
in another form. My son has seen these things
a number of times, and knows what to expect;
he does not seem disturbed or anything more
than mildly amused. Maybe these old cartoons
refer to my childhood and not to his
(The ogres in them wear Mussolini's face),
so that when mice are swallowed by skeletons
or empty suits of armor, when a tribe

of savage Negro mice is put through a wringer
and stacked flat in the cellar, he can take
the objective and critical view, while I
am shaken to see the giant picassoid
parents eating and voiding their little mice
time and again. And when the cheery announcer
cries, "Well, kids, that's the end," my son gets up
obediently and runs outside to play.
I hope he will ride over this world as well,
and that his crudest and most terrifying dreams
will not return with such wide publicity.

HOWARD NEMEROV

Where Are You Now, Batman?

Where are you now, Batman? Now that Aunt Heriot has
    reported Robin missing
And Superman's fallen asleep in the sixpenny childhood seats?
Where are you now that Captain Marvel's SHAZAM! echoes
    round the auditorium,
The magicians don't hear it,
Must all be deaf . . . or dead . . .
The Purple Monster who came down from the Purple Planet
    disguised as a man
Is wandering aimlessly about the streets
With no way of getting back.
Sir Galahad's been strangled by the Incredible Living Trees,
Zorro killed by his own sword.
Blackhawk has buried the last of his companions
And has now gone off to commit suicide in the disused
    Hangars of Innocence
The Monster and the Ape still fight it out in a room
Where the walls are continually closing in;
Rocketman's fuel tanks gave out over London.
Even Flash Gordon's lost, he wanders among the stars
Weeping over the woman he loved
7 Universes ago.
    My celluloid companions, it's only a few years
Since I knew you. Something in us has faded.
    Has the Terrible Fiend, That Ghastly Adversary,
Mr Old Age, Caught you in his deadly trap,
And come finally to polish you off,
His machinegun dripping with years . . . ?

BRIAN PATTEN

Pass Office Song

The scene is any pass office, where all male Africans must go to get their Registration Certificates. There they must wait in queues for hours and sometimes for days before they are attended to. It is a regulation which rankles in their minds and so they sing about it.

Take off your hat.
What is your home name?
Who is your father?
Who is your chief?
Where do you pay your tax?
What river do you drink?
We mourn for our country.

ANONYMOUS Transcribed by Peggy Rutherfoord

The Mouth and the Body

I passed along a quiet street
The mouth said a word
A man came and beat me
The mouth abused a lady
I was imprisoned.

Mouth, mouth, mouth
Always you act and I'm repaid
Once we shall meet
In a boxing ring
Then you start speaking and let me react
And you'll feel what I feel.

PHILIP MWANIKIH Age 14 Kenya

A Living

A man should never earn his living,
if he earns his life he'll be lovely.

A bird
picks up its seeds or little snails
between heedless earth and heaven
in heedlessness.

But, the plucky little sport, it gives to life
song, and chirruping, gay feathers, fluff-shadowed warmth
and all the unspeakable charm of birds hopping and fluttering
    and being birds.
— And we, we get it all from them for nothing.

D. H. LAWRENCE

On Hurricane Jackson

Now his nose's bridge is broken, one eye
will not focus and the other is a stray;
trainers whisper in his mouth while one ear
listens to itself, clenched like a fist;
generally shadow-boxing in a smoky room,
his mind hides like the aching boys
who lost a contest in the Pan-Hellenic games
and had to take the back roads home,
but someone else, his perfect youth,
laureled in newsprint and dollar bills,
triumphs forever on the great white way
to the statistical Sparta of the champs.

ALAN DUGAN

What Is He?

What is he?
— A man, of course.
Yes, but what does he do?
— He lives and is a man.
Oh quite! but he must work. He must have a job of some sort.
— Why?
Because obviously he's not one of the leisured classes.
— I don't know. He has lots of leisure. And he makes quite
   beautiful chairs. —
There you are then! He's a cabinet maker.
— No no!
Anyhow a carpenter and joiner.
— Not at all.
But you said so.
— What did I say?
That he made chairs, and was a joiner and carpenter.
— I said he made chairs, but I did not say he was a carpenter.
All right then, he's just an amateur.
— Perhaps! Would you say a thrush was a professional flautist,
   or just an amateur? —
I'd say it was just a bird.
— And I say he is just a man.
All right! You always did quibble.

D. H. LAWRENCE

Buyers and Sellers

What is a man worth?
What can he do?
What is his value?
On the one hand those who buy labor,
On the other hand those who have nothing
    to sell but their labor.
And when the buyers of labor tell the
    sellers, "Nothing doing today, not a
    chance!" — then what?

CARL SANDBURG

My Busconductor

My busconductor tells me
he only has one kidney
and that may soon go on strike
through overwork.
Each busticket
takes on now a different shape
and texture.
He holds a ninepenny single
as if it were a rose
and puts the shilling in his bag
as a child into a gasmeter.
His thin lips
have no quips
for fat factorygirls
and he ignores
the drunk who snores
and the oldman who talks to himself
and gets off at the wrong stop.
He goes gently to the bedroom
of the bus
to collect
and watch familiar shops and pubs passby
(perhaps for the last time?)
The sameold streets look different now
more distinct
as through new glasses.
And the sky
was it ever so blue?

And all the time
deepdown in the deserted busshelter of his mind
he thinks about his journey nearly done.
One day he'll clock on and never clock off
or clock off and never clock on.

ROGER McGOUGH

To an Athlete Dying Young

The time you won your town the race
We chaired you through the marketplace;
Man and boy stood cheering by,
And home we brought you shoulder-high.

Today, the road all runners come,
Shoulder-high we bring you home,
And set you at your threshold down,
Townsman of a stiller town.

Smart lad, to slip betimes away
From fields where glory does not stay,
And early though the laurel grows,
It withers quicker than the rose.

Eyes the shady night has shut
Cannot see the record cut,
And silence sounds no worse than cheers
After earth has stopped the ears:

Now you will not swell the rout
Of lads that wore their honours out,
Runners whom renown outran
And the name died before the man.

So set, before its echoes fade,
The fleet foot on the sill of shade,
And hold to the low lintel up
The still-defended challenge-cup.

And round that early-laurelled head
Will flock to gaze the strengthless dead,
And find unwithered on its curls
The garland briefer than a girl's.

A. E. HOUSMAN

Fern Hill

Now as I was young and easy under the apple boughs
About the lilting house and happy as the grass was green,
    The night above the dingle starry,
      Time let me hail and climb
    Golden in the heydays of his eyes,
And honored among wagons I was prince of the apple towns
And once below a time I lordly had the trees and leaves
      Trail with daisies and barley
    Down the rivers of the windfall light.

And as I was green and carefree, famous among the barns
About the happy yard and singing as the farm was home,
    In the sun that is young once only,
      Time let me play and be
    Golden in the mercy of his means,
And green and golden I was huntsman and herdsman, the
          calves
Sang to my horn, the foxes on the hills barked clear and cold,
      And the sabbath rang slowly
    In the pebbles of the holy streams.

All the sun long it was running, it was lovely, the hay
Fields high as the house, the tunes from the chimneys, it
         was air
    And playing, lovely and watery
      And fire green as grass.
    And nightly under the simple stars
As I rode to sleep the owls were bearing the farm away,
All the moon long I heard, blessed among stables, the night-
      jars
    Flying with the ricks, and the horses
      Flashing into the dark.

And then to awake, and the farm, like a wanderer white
With the dew, come back, the cock on his shoulder: it was all
    Shining, it was Adam and maiden,
         The sky gathered again
    And the sun grew round that very day.
So it must have been after the birth of the simple light
In the first, spinning place, the spellbound horses walking
         warm
    Out of the whinnying green stable
      On to the fields of praise.

And honored among foxes and pheasants by the gay house
Under the new made clouds and happy as the heart was long,
    In the sun born over and over,
      I ran my heedless ways,
      My wishes raced through the house high hay
And nothing I cared, at my sky blue trades, that time allows
In all his tuneful turning so few and such morning songs
    Before the children green and golden
      Follow him out of grace,

Nothing I cared, in the lamb white days, that time would
      take me
Up to the swallow thronged loft by the shadow of my hand,
    In the moon that is always rising,
      Nor that riding to sleep
    I should hear him fly with the high fields
And wake to the farm forever fled from the childless land.
Oh as I was young and easy in the mercy of his means,
      Time held me green and dying
    Though I sang in my chains like the sea.

DYLAN THOMAS

Ex-Basketball Player

Pearl Avenue runs past the high school lot,
Bends with the trolley tracks, and stops, cut off
Before it has a chance to go two blocks,
At Colonel McComsky Plaza. Berth's Garage
Is on the corner facing west, and there,
Most days, you'll find Flick Webb, who helps Berth out.

Flick stands tall among the idiot pumps —
Five on a side, the old bubble-head style,
Their rubber elbows hanging loose and low.
One's nostrils are two S's, and his eyes
An E and O. And one is squat, without
A head at all — more of a football type.

Once, Flick played for the high school team, the Wizards.
He was good: in fact, the best. In '46,
He bucketed three hundred ninety points,
A county record still. The ball loved Flick.
I saw him rack up thirty-eight or forty
In one home game. His hands were like wild birds.

He never learned a trade; he just sells gas,
Checks oil, and changes flats. Once in a while,
As a gag, he dribbles an inner tube,
But most of us remember anyway.
His hands are fine and nervous on the lug wrench.
It makes no difference to the lug wrench, though.

Off work, he hangs around Mae's Luncheonette.
Grease-grey and kind of coiled, he plays pinball,
Sips lemon cokes, and smokes those thin cigars;
Flick seldom speaks to Mae, just sits and nods
Beyond her face towards bright applauding tiers
Of Necco Wafers, Nibs, and Juju Beads.

JOHN UPDIKE

Cobb Would Have Caught It

In sunburnt parks where Sundays lie
Or the wide wastes beyond the cities,
Teams in grey deploy through sunlight.

Talk it up, boys, a little practice.

Coming in stubby and fast, the baseman
Gathers a grounder in fat green grass,
Picks it stinging and clipped as wit
Into the leather: a swinging step
Wings it deadeye down to first.
Smack. Oh, attaboy, attyoldboy.
Catcher reverses his cap, pulls down
Sweaty casque, and squats in the dust:
Pitcher rubs new ball on his pants,
Chewing, puts a jet behind him;
Nods past batter, taking his time.
Batter settles, tugs at his cap:
A spinning ball: step and swing to it,
Caught like a cheek before it ducks
By shivery hickory: socko, baby:
Cleats dig into dust. Outfielder,
On his way, looking over shoulder,
Makes it a triple. A long peg home.

Innings and afternoons. Fly lost in sunset.
Throwing arm gone bad. There's your old ball game.
Cool reek of the field. Reek of companions.

ROBERT FITZGERALD

Fame If Not Fortune

A half-dollar in the hand of a gypsy
    tells me this and more:
You shall go broken on the wheel,
      lashed to the bars and fates of steel,
      a nickel's worth of nothing,
      a vaudeville gag,
      a child's busted rubber balloon kicked
         amid dirty bunting and empty popcorn
         bags at a summer park.
Yet cigarmakers shall name choice Havanas and
    paste your picture on the box,
Racehorses foaming under scarlet and ochre jockeys
    shall wear your name,
And policemen direct strangers to parks and schools
    remembered after you.

CARL SANDBURG

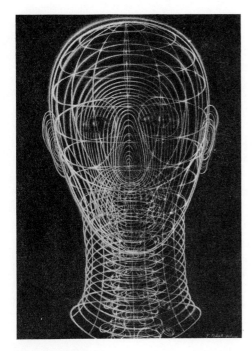

Head VI, colored pencil on black paper, by Pavel
Tchelitchew. The Museum of Modern Art,
New York

Soup

I saw a famous man eating soup.
I say he was lifting a fat broth
Into his mouth with a spoon.
His name was in the newspapers that day
Spelled out in tall black headlines
And thousands of people were talking about him.

    When I saw him,
He sat bending his head over a plate
Putting soup in his mouth with a spoon.

CARL SANDBURG

Epitaph on a Tryant

Perfection, of a kind, was what he was after,
And the poetry he invented was easy to understand;
He knew human folly like the back of his hand,
And was greatly interested in armies and fleets;
When he laughed, respectable senators burst with laughter,
And when he cried the little children died in the streets.

W. H. AUDEN

Leader of Men

When he addressed ten thousand
Faces worked by automation
He was filled, exalted, afflated
With love and ambition for
His fellowcountrymen — in so far,
Of course,
As they were not incompatible
With the love and ambition he felt
For himself. No sacrifice
Would be too great. No

Holocaust. No bloodbath. He
Was affected by the nobility
Of his vision, his eyes were,
Naturally, blurred.

How was he to know
The mindless face of the crowd
Broke up, when he finished, into
Ten thousand pieces — except that,
When he went home,
He found the tea cold, his wife
Plain, his dogs smelly?

NORMAN MacCAIG

The Hand That Signed the Paper

The hand that signed the paper felled a city;
Five sovereign fingers taxed the breath,
Doubled the globe of dead and halved a country;
These five kings did a king to death.

The mighty hand leads to a sloping shoulder,
The finger joints are cramped with chalk;
A goose's quill has put an end to murder
That put an end to talk.

The hand that signed the treaty bred a fever,
And famine grew, and locusts came;
Great is the hand that holds dominion over
Man by a scribbled name.

The five kings count the dead but do not soften
The crusted wound nor stroke the brow;
A hand rules pity as a hand rules heaven;
Hands have no tears to flow.

DYLAN THOMAS

47

Is Wisdom a Lot of Language?

Apes, may I speak to you a moment?
Chimpanzees, come hither for words.
Orangoutangs, let's get into a huddle.
Baboons, lemme whisper in your ears.
Gorillas, do yuh hear me hollerin' to yuh?
And monkeys! monkeys! get this chatter —

> For a long time men have plucked letters
> Out of the air and shaped syllables.
> And out of the syllables came words
> And from the words came phrases, clauses.
> Sentences were born — and languages.
> (The Tower of Babel didn't work out —
> it came down quicker than it went up.)
> Misunderstandings followed the languages,
> Arguments, epithets, maledictions, curses,
> Gossip, backbiting, the buzz of the bazoo,
> Chit chat, blah blah, talk just to be talking,
> Monologues of members telling other members
> How good they are now and were yesterday,
> Conversations missing the point,
> Dialogues seldom as beautiful as soliloquies,
> Seldom as fine as a man alone, a woman by herself
> Telling a clock, "I'm a plain damn fool."

Read the dictionary from A to Izzard today.
Get a vocabulary. Brush up on your diction.
See whether wisdom is just a lot of language.

CARL SANDBURG

The Fall of the Tower of Babel

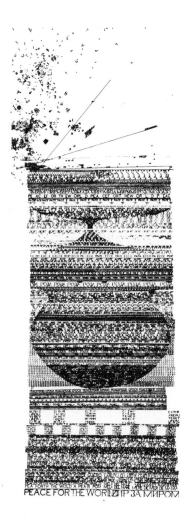

JOHN FURNIVAL

next to of course god america i

"next to of course god america i
love you land of the pilgrims' and so forth oh
say can you see by the dawn's early my
country 'tis of centuries come and go
and are no more what of it we should worry
in every language even deafanddumb
thy sons acclaim your glorious name by gorry
by jingo by gee by gosh by gum
why talk of beauty what could be more beautiful than these heroic happy dead
who rushed like lions to the roaring slaughter
they did not stop to think they died instead
then shall the voice of liberty be mute?"

He spoke. And drank rapidly a glass of water

E. E. CUMMINGS

a politician is an arse upon

a politician is an arse upon
which everyone has sat except a man

E. E. CUMMINGS

Girl Marcher

Now *Ban The Bomb!* I'm with you, though we fail.
Did *Ban The Arrow! Ban The Fist!* avail?
Still the red lips, ecstatic, cry "Ban! Ban!"
First ban yourself, sweet marcher. Banish man.

JOHN FREDERICK NIMS

Don't Sign Anything

Riding the horse as was my wont,
there was a bunch of cows in a field.

The horse
chased

them. I likewise, an uneasy
accompanist.

To wit, the Chinese proverb goes:
if you lie in a field

and fall asleep,
you will be found in a field

asleep.

ROBERT CREELEY

I'm Older Than You, Please Listen

To the young man I would say:
Get out! Look sharp, my boy,
before the roots are down,
before the equations are struck,
before a face or a landscape
has power to shape or destroy.
This land is a lump without leaven,
a body that has no nerves.
Don't be content to live in
a sort of second-grade heaven
with first-grade butter, fresh air,
and paper in every toilet;
becoming a butt for the malice
of those who have stayed and soured,
staying in turn to sour,
to smile, and savage the young.
If you're enterprising and able,
smuggle your talents away,
hawk them in livelier markets
where people are willing to pay.
If you have no stomach for roughage,
if patience isn't your religion,
if you must have sherry with your bitters,
if money and fame are your pigeon,
if you feel that you need success
and long for a good address,
don't anchor here in the desert —
the fishing isn't so good:
take a ticket for Megalopolis,
don't stay in this neighbourhood!

A. R. D. FAIRBURN

Ballad of the Bread Man

Mary stood in the kitchen
Baking a loaf of bread.
An angel flew in through the window.
We've a job for you, he said.

God in his big gold heaven,
Sitting in his big blue chair,
Wanted a mother for his little son.
Suddenly saw you there.

Mary shook and trembled,
It isn't true what you say.
Don't say that, said the angel.
The baby's on its way.

Joseph was in the workshop
Planing a piece of wood.
The old man's past it, the neighbors said.
That girl's been up to no good.

And who was that elegant fellow,
They said, in the shiny gear?
The things they said about Gabriel
Were hardly fit to hear.

Mary never answered,
Mary never replied.
She kept the information,
Like the baby, safe inside.

It was election winter.
They went to vote in town.
When Mary found her time had come
The hotels let her down.

The baby was born in an annex
Next to the local pub.
At midnight, a delegation
Turned up from the Farmer's Club.

They talked about an explosion
That made a hole in the sky,
Said they'd been sent to the Lamb & Flag
To see god come down from on high.

A few days later a bishop
And a five-star general were seen
With the head of an African country
In a bullet-proof limousine.

We've come, they said, with tokens
For the little boy to choose.
Told the tale about war and peace
In the television news.

After them came the soldiers
With rifle and bomb and gun,
Looking for enemies of the state.
The family had packed and gone.

When they got back to the village
The neighbors said to a man,
That boy will never be one of us,
Though he does what he blessed well can.

He went round to all the people
A paper crown on his head.
Here is some bread from my father.
Take, eat, he said.

Nobody seemed very hungry,
Nobody seemed to care.
Nobody saw the god in himself
Quietly standing there.

He finished up in the papers.
He came to a very bad end.
He was charged with bringing the living to life.
No man was that prisoner's friend.

There's only one kind of punishment
To fit that kind of a crime.
They rigged a trial and shot him dead.
They were only just in time.

They lifted the young man by the leg,
They lifted him by the arm,
They locked him in a cathedral
In case he came to harm.

They stored him safe as water
Under seven rocks.
One Sunday morning he burst out
Like a jack-in-the-box.

Through the town he went walking.
He showed them the holes in his head.
Now do you want any loaves? he cried.
Not today, they said.

CHARLES CAUSLEY

a man who had fallen among thieves

a man who had fallen among thieves
lay by the roadside on his back
dressed in fifteenthrate ideas
wearing a round jeer for a hat

fate per a somewhat more than less
emancipated evening
had in return for consciousness
endowed him with a changeless grin

whereon a dozen staunch and leal
citizens did graze at pause
then fired by hypercivic zeal
sought newer pastures or because

swaddled with a frozen brook
of pinkest vomit out of eyes
which noticed nobody he looked
as if he did not care to rise

one hand did nothing on the vest
its wideflung friend clenched weakly dirt
while the mute trouserfly confessed
a button solemnly inert.

Brushing from whom the stiffened puke
i put him all into my arms
and staggered banged with terror through
a million billion trillion stars

E. E. CUMMINGS

since feeling is first

since feeling is first
who pays any attention
to the syntax of things
will never wholly kiss you;

wholly to be a fool
while Spring is in the world

my blood approves,
and kisses are a better fate
than wisdom
lady i swear by all flowers. Don't cry
— the best gesture of my brain is less than
your eyelids' flutter which says

we are for each other: then
laugh, leaning back in my arms
for life's not a paragraph

And death i think is no parenthesis

E. E. CUMMINGS

Dreaming Fool

I was the first of the fools
(So I dreamed)
And all the fools of the world
    were put into me and I was
    the biggest fool of all.

Others were fools in the morning
Or in the evening or on Saturdays
Or odd days like Friday the Thirteenth
But me — I was a fool every day in the week
And when asleep I was the sleeping fool.
(So I dreamed.)

CARL SANDBURG

Strawberries

There were never strawberries
like the ones we had
that sultry afternoon
sitting on the step
of the open french window
facing each other
your knees held in mine
the blue plates in our laps
the strawberries glistening
in the hot sunlight
we dipped them in sugar
looking at each other
not hurrying the feast
for one to come
the empty plates
laid on the stone together
with the two forks crossed
and I bent towards you
sweet in that air
in my arms
abandoned like a child
from your eager mouth
the taste of strawberries
in my memory
lean back again
let me love you
let the sun beat
on our forgetfulness
one hour of all
the heat intense
and summer lightning
on the Kilpatrick hills

let the storm wash the plates

EDWIN MORGAN

The Passionate Shepherd to His Love

Come live with me and be my Love,
And we will all the pleasures prove
That hills and valleys, dales and fields,
Or woods or steepy mountain yields.

And we will sit upon the rocks,
And see the shepherds feed their flocks
By shallow rivers, to whose falls
Melodious birds sing madrigals.

And I will make thee beds of roses
And a thousand fragrant posies;
A cap of flowers, and a kirtle
Embroider'd all with leaves of myrtle.

A gown made of the finest wool
Which from our pretty lambs we pull;
Fair-linéd slippers for the cold,
With buckles of the purest gold.

A belt of straw and ivy-buds
With coral clasps and amber studs:
And if these pleasures may thee move,
Come live with me and be my Love.

The shepherd swains shall dance and sing
For thy delight each May morning:
If these delights thy mind may move,
Then live with me and be my Love.

CHRISTOPHER MARLOWE

The Nymph's Reply to the Shepherd

If all the world and love were young,
And truth in every shepherd's tongue,
These pretty pleasures might me move,
To live with thee, and be thy love.

Time drives the flocks from field to fold,
When Rivers rage, and Rocks grow cold,
And Philomel becometh dumb,
The rest complains of cares to come.

The flowers do fade, and wanton fields
To wayward winter reckoning yields,
A honey tongue, a heart of gall,
Is fancy's spring, but sorrow's fall.

Thy gowns, thy shoes, thy beds of Roses,
Thy cap, thy kirtle, and thy posies,
Soon break, soon wither, soon forgotten:
In folly ripe, in reason rotten.

Thy belt of straw and Ivy buds,
Thy Coral clasps and Amber studs,
All these in me no means can move,
To come to thee, and be thy love.

But could youth last, and love still breed,
Had joys no date, nor age no need,
Then these delights my mind might move,
To live with thee, and be thy love.

SIR WALTER RALEIGH

Come, Live with Me and Be My Love

Come, live with me and be my love,
And we will all the pleasures prove
Of peace and plenty, bed and board,
That chance employment may afford.

I'll handle dainties on the docks
And thou shalt read of summer frocks:
At evening by the sour canals
We'll hope to hear some madrigals.

Care on thy maiden brow shall put
A wreath of wrinkles, and thy foot
Be shod with pain: not silken dress
But toil shall tire thy loveliness.

Hunger shall make thy modest zone
And cheat fond death of all but bone —
If these delights thy mind may move,
Then live with me and be my love.

C. DAY LEWIS

When You're Away

When you're away, I'm restless, lonely,
Wretched, bored, dejected; only
Here's the rub, my darling dear,
I feel the same when you are near.

SAMUEL HOFFENSTEIN

A Gentle Echo on Woman

Shepherd: Echo, I ween, will in the wood reply,
　　　　　And quaintly answer questions; shall I try?
Echo: 　　　　　　　　Try.

Shepherd: What must we do our passion to express?
Echo: 　　　　　　　　Press.

Shepherd: What most moves women when we them address?
Echo: 　　　　　　　　A dress.

Shepherd: If music soften rocks, love tunes my lyre.
Echo: 　　　　　　　　Liar.

Shepherd: Then teach me, Echo, how shall I come by her?
Echo: 　　　　　　　　Buy her.

Shepherd: When bought, no question I shall be her dear?
Echo: 　　　　　　　　Her deer.

Shepherd: But what can glad me when she's laid on bier?
Echo: 　　　　　　　　Beer.

Shepherd: What must I do when women will be kind?
Echo: 　　　　　　　　Be kind.

Shepherd: What must I do when women will be cross?
Echo: 　　　　　　　　Be cross.

Shepherd: Lord, what is she that can so turn and wind?
Echo: 　　　　　　　　Wind.

Shepherd: If she be wind, what stills her when she blows?
Echo: 　　　　　　　　Blows.

Shepherd: But if she bang again, still should I bang her?
Echo: 　　　　　　　　Bang her.

Shepherd: Is there no way to moderate her anger?
Echo: 　　　　　　　　Hang her.

Shepherd: Thanks, gentle Echo! right thy answers tell
　　　　　What woman is and how to guard her well.
Echo: 　　　　　　　　Guard her well.

JONATHAN SWIFT

Fire and Ice

Some say the world will end in fire,
Some say in ice.
From what I've tasted of desire
I hold with those who favor fire.
But if it had to perish twice,
I think I know enough of hate
To say that for destruction ice
Is also great
And would suffice.

ROBERT FROST

One Hard Look

Small gnats that fly
In hot July
And lodge in sleeping ears
Can rouse therein
A trumpet's din
With Day of Judgment fears.

Small mice at night
Can wake more fright
Than lions at midday;
A straw will crack
The camel's back —
There is no easier way.

One smile relieves
A heart that grieves
Though deadly sad it be,
And one hard look
Can close the book
That lovers love to see.

ROBERT GRAVES

Parting, Without a Sequel

She has finished and sealed the letter
At last, which he so richly has deserved,
With characters venomous and hatefully curved,
And nothing could be better.

But even as she gave it
Saying to the blue-capped functioner of doom,
"Into his hands," she hoped the leering groom
Might somewhere lose and leave it.

Then all the blood
Forsook the face. She was too pale for tears,
Observing the ruin of her younger years.
She went and stood

Under her father's vaunting oak
Who kept his peace in wind and sun, and glistened
Stoical in the rain; to whom she listened
If he spoke.

And now the agitation of the rain
Rasped his sere leaves, and he talked low and gentle
Reproaching the wan daughter by the lintel;
Ceasing and beginning again.

Away went the messenger's bicycle,
His serpent's track went up the hill forever,
And all the time she stood there hot as fever
And cold as any icicle.

JOHN CROWE RANSOM

Pomander

pomander
open pomander
open poem and her
open poem and him
open poem and hymn
hymn and hymen leander
high man pen meander
o pen poem me and her
pen me poem me and him
om mane padme hum
pad me home panda hand
open up o holy panhandler
ample panda pen or bamboo pond
ponder a bonny poem pomander opener
open banned peon penman hum and banter
open hymn and pompom band and panda hamper
o i am a pen open man or happener
i am open manner happener
happy are we open
poem and a pom
poem and a panda
poem and aplomb

EDWIN MORGAN

Ballad

A faithless shepherd courted me,
He stole away my liberty;
When my poor heart was strange to men
He came and smiled and stole it then.

When my apron would hang low
Me he sought through frost and snow;
When it puckered up with shame
And I sought him, he never came.

When summer brought no fears to fright,
He came to guard me every night;
When winter nights did darkly prove,
None came to guard me or to love.

I wish, I wish — but it's in vain —
I wish I was a maid again;
A maid again I cannot be:
O when will green grass cover me?

I wish my babe had ne'er been born;
I've made its pillow on a thorn.
I wish my sorrows all away,
My soul with God, my body clay.

He promised beds as fine as silk
And sheets for love as white as milk
But he when won my heart astray
Left me to want a bed of clay.

He kept his sheep on yonder hill,
His heart seemed soft but it was steel;
I ran with love and was undone,
O had I walked ere I did run.

He has two hearts and I have none;
He'll be a rogue, when I am gone,
To thee, my baby, unto thee,
As he has been too long to me.

I weep the past, I dread the gloom
Of sorrows in the time to come;
When thou without a friend shalt be
Weeping on a stranger's knee.

My heart would break — but it is brass —
To see thee smile upon my face,
To see thee smile at words that be
The messengers of grief to thee.

I wish, my child, thou'dst ne'er been born,
I've made thy pillow on a thorn;
I wish our sorrows both away,
Our souls with God, our bodies clay.

TRADITIONAL

A Thousand Years

A thousand years, you said,
As our hearts melted.
I look at the hand you held,
And the ache is hard to bear.

LADY HEGURI Translated from the Japanese by Geoffrey Bownas and Anthony Thwaite

My Tangled Hair

My tangled hair
I shall not cut:
Your hand, my dearest,
Touched it as a pillow.

ANONYMOUS Translated from the Japanese by Geoffrey Bownas and Anthony Thwaite

Cat-Goddesses

A perverse habit of cat-goddesses —
Even the blackest of them, black as coals
Save for a new moon blazing on each breast,
With coral tongues and beryl eyes like lamps,
Long-leggéd, pacing three by three in nines —
This obstinate habit is to yield themselves,
In verisimilar love-ecstasies,
To tatter-eared and slinking alley-toms
No less below the common run of cats
Than they above it; which they do for spite,
To provoke jealousy — not the least abashed
By such gross-headed, rabbit-colored litters
As soon they shall be happy to desert.

ROBERT GRAVES

Chinese Cat

p m r k g n i a o u
p m r k g n i a o
p m r k n i a o
p m r n i a o
p m r i a o
p m i a o
m i a o
m a o

EDWIN MORGAN

Cat-Faith

As a cat, caught by the door opening,
on the perilous top shelf, red-jawed and raspberry-clawed,
lets itself fall floorward without looking,
sure by cat-instinct it will find the ground
where innocence is; and falls
anyhow, in a furball, so fast that the eye
misses the twist and trust
that come from having fallen before,
and only notices cat silking away,
crime inconceivable in so meek a walk,

so do we let ourselves fall morningward
through shelves of dream. When, libertine at dark,
we let the visions in, and the black window
grotesques us back, our world unbalances.
Many-faced monsters of our own devising
jostle at the verge of sleep, as the room
loses its edges and grows hazed and haunted
by words murmured or by woes remembered,
till, sleep-dissolved, we fall, the known world leaves us,
and room and dream and self and safety melt
into a final madness, where any landscape
may easily curdle, and the dead cry out . . .

but ultimately, it ebbs. Voices recede.
The pale square of the window glows and stays.
Slowly the room arrives and dawns, and we
arrive in our selves. Last night, last week, the past
leak back, awake. As light solidifies,
dream dims. Outside, the washed hush of the garden
waits patiently, and, newcomers from death,
how gratefully we draw its breath!
Yet, to endure that unknown night by night,
must we not be sure, with cat-insight,
we can afford its terrors, and that full day
will find us at the desk, sane, unafraid —
cheeks shaven, letters written, bills paid?

ALASTAIR REID

The Groundhog

In June, amid the golden fields,
I saw a groundhog lying dead,
Dead lay he; my senses shook,
And mind outshot our naked frailty.
There lowly in the vigorous summer
His form began its senseless change,
And made my senses waver dim
Seeing nature ferocious in him.
Inspecting close his maggots' might
And seething cauldron of his being,
Half with loathing, half with a strange love,
I poked him with an angry stick.
The fever arose, became a flame
and Vigour circumscribed the skies,
Immense energy in the sun,
And through my frame a sunless trembling.
My stick had done nor good nor harm.
Then stood I silent in the day
Watching the object, as before;
And kept my reverence for knowledge
Trying for control, to be still,
To quell the passion of the blood;
Until I had bent down on my knees
Praying for joy in the sight of decay.
And so I left; and I returned
In Autumn strict of eye, to see
The sap gone out of the groundhog,
But the bony sodden hulk remained.
But the year had lost its meaning,
And in intellectual chains
I lost both love and loathing,
Mured up in the wall of wisdom.
Another summer took the fields again
Massive and burning, full of life,

But when I chanced upon the spot
There was only a little hair left,
And bones bleaching in the sunlight
Beautiful as architecture;
I watched them like a geometer,
And cut a walking stick from a birch.
It has been three years now.
There is no sign of the groundhog.
I stood there in the whirling summer,
My hand capped a withered heart,
And thought of China and of Greece,
Of Alexander in his tent;
Of Montaigne in his tower,
Of Saint Theresa in her wild lament.

RICHARD EBERHART

The Red Cockatoo

Sent as a present from Annam —
A red cockatoo.
Coloured like the peach-tree blossom,
Speaking with the speech of men.
And they did to it what is always done
To the learned and eloquent.
They took a cage with stout bars
And shut it up inside.

ANONYMOUS Translated from the Chinese by Arthur Waley

Hurt Hawks

The broken pillar of the wing jags from the clotted shoulder,
The wing trails like a banner in defeat,
No more to use the sky forever but live with famine
And pain a few days: cat nor coyote
Will shorten the week of waiting for death, there is game
    without talons.
He stands under the oak-bush and waits
The lame feet of salvation; at night he remembers freedom
And flies in a dream, the dawns ruin it.
He is strong and pain is worse to the strong, incapacity is
    worse
The curs of the day come and torment him
At distance, no one but death the redeemer will humble that
    head,
The intrepid readiness, the terrible eyes.
The wild God of the world is sometimes merciful to those
That ask mercy, not often to the arrogant.
You do not know him, you communal people, or you have
    forgotten him;
Intemperate and savage, the hawk remembers him;
Beautiful and wild, the hawks, and men that are dying,
    remember him.
I'd sooner, except the penalties, kill a man than a hawk; but
    the great redtail
Had nothing left but unable misery
From the bone too shattered for mending, the wing that trailed
    under his talons when he moved.
We had fed him six weeks, I gave him freedom,
He wandered over the foreland hill and returned in the
    evening, asking for death,
Not like a beggar, still eyed with the old
Implacable arrogance. I gave him the lead gift in the twilight.
    What fell was relaxed,
Owl-downy, soft feminine feathers; but what
Soared: the fierce rush: the night-herons by the flooded river
    cried for fear at its rising
Before it was quite unsheathed from reality.

ROBINSON JEFFERS

Pigeons

On the crooked arm of Columbus, on his cloak,
they mimic his blind and statuary stare,
and the chipped profiles of his handmaidens
they adorn with droppings. Over the loud square,
from all the arms and ledges of their rest,
only a bread crust or a bell unshelves them.
Adding to Atlas' globe, they dispose themselves
with a fat propriety, and pose as garlands
importantly about his burdened shoulders.
Occasionally a lift of wind uncarves them.

   Stone becomes them; they, in their turn, become it.
Their opal eyes have a monumental cast.
And, in a maze of noise,
their quiet *croomb croomb* dignifies the spaces,
suggesting the sound of silence. On cobbled islands,
marooned in tantrums of traffic, they know their place,
faithful and anonymous, like servants,
and never beg, but properly receive.

   Arriving in rainbows of oil-and-water feathers,
they fountain down from buttresses and outcrops,
from Fontainebleau and London,
and, squat on the margins of roofs, with a gargoyle look,
they note, from an edge of air, with hooded eyes,
the city slowly lessening the sky.

   All praise to them who nightly in the parks
keep peace for us; who, cosmopolitan,
patrol and people all cathedraled places,
and easily, lazily haunt and inhabit
St Paul's, St Peter's, or the Madeleine,
the paved courts of the past, pompous as keepers —
a sober race of messengers and custodians,
neat in their international uniforms,
alighting with a word perhaps from Rome.
Permanence is their business, space and time
their special preservations; and wherever
the great stone men we save from death are stationed,
appropriately on the head of each is perched,
as though for ever, his appointed pigeon.

ALASTAIR REID

City Number

The soiled city oblongs stand sprawling.
The blocks and house numbers go miles.
Trucks howl rushing the early morning editions.
Night-club dancers have done their main floor show.
Tavern trios improvise "Show me the way to go home."
Soldiers and sailors look for street corners, house numbers.
Night watchmen figure halfway between midnight and breakfast.
Look out the window now late after the evening that was.
    On a south sky of pigeon-egg blue
    Long clouds float in a silver moonbath.

CARL SANDBURG

Fortune Has Its Cookies

               Fortune
                     has its cookies to give out

which is a good thing

                     since it's been a long, time since

           that summer in Brooklyn
       when they closed off the street
            one hot day
             and the

                           FIREMEN

                               turned on their hoses
        and all the kids ran out in it

           in the middle of the street

        and there were

                maybe a couple dozen of us

                        out there

with the water squirting up
                    to the

            sky

                        and all over
                                us
        there was maybe only six of us
                            kids altogether
            running around in our
                            barefeet and birthday
        suits
                    and I remember Molly but then
        the firemen stopped squirting their hoses
            all of a sudden and went
                    back in
                    their firehouse
                    and
            started playing pinochle again
                just as if nothing
                had ever
                            happened
    while I remember Molly
                    looked at me and

        ran in

    because I guess really we were the only ones there

LAWRENCE FERLINGHETTI

Summer Haiku

P ool.
Pe opl
e plop!
Cool.

EDWIN MORGAN

Morning at the Window

They are rattling breakfast plates in basement kitchens,
And along the trampled edges of the street
I am aware of the damp souls of housemaids
Sprouting despondently at area gates.

The brown waves of fog toss up to me
Twisted faces from the bottom of the street,
And tear from a passer-by with muddy skirts
An aimless smile that hovers in the air
And vanishes along the level of the roofs.

T. S. ELIOT

Preludes

1   The winter evening settles down
With smell of steaks in passageways.
Six o'clock.
The burnt-out ends of smoky days.
And now a gusty shower wraps
The grimy scraps
Of withered leaves about your feet
And newspapers from vacant lots;
The showers beat
On broken blinds and chimney-pots,
And at the corner of the street
A lonely cab-horse steams and stamps.
And then the lighting of the lamps.

2   The morning comes to consciousness
Of faint stale smells of beer
From the sawdust-trampled street
With all its muddy feet that press
To early coffee-stands.
With the other masquerades
That time resumes,
One thinks of all the hands
That are raising dingy shades
In a thousand furnished rooms.

82

T. S. ELIOT

Tribute to Henry Ford   1

RICHARD KOSTELANETZ

Ɐ Ɐ
  Ɐ

Ɐ Ɐ
  Ɐ
  Ɐ
Ɐ Ɐ

A A
A A
  A
A A
  A
A A

RICHARD KOSTELANETZ

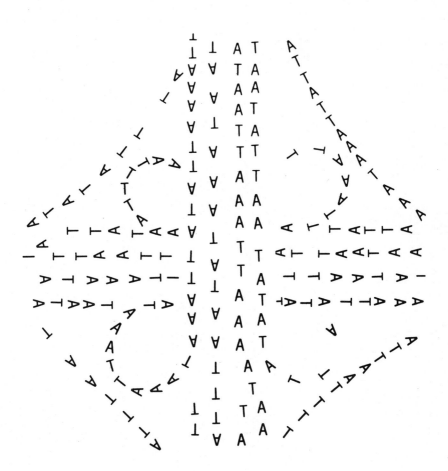

RICHARD KOSTELANETZ

Transcontinent

Where the cities end, the
dumps grow the oil-can shacks
from Portland, Maine,

to Seattle. Broken
cars rust in Troy, New York,
and Cleveland Heights.

On the train, the people
eat candy bars, and watch,
or fall asleep.

When they look outside and
see cars and shacks, they know
they're nearly there.

DONALD HALL

Vacation

One scene as I bow to pour her coffee: —

Three Indians in the scouring drouth
huddle at a grave scooped in the gravel,
lean to the wind as our train goes by.
Someone is gone.
There is dust on everything in Nevada.

I pour the cream.

WILLIAM STAFFORD

Orgy

```
c a n t e r c a n t e r c a n t e r c a n t e r
a n t e a t e r a n t e a t e r a n t e a t e r
a n t e n c o u n t e r a n t e n c o u n t e r
a n t e n n a r e a c t a n t e n n a r e a c t
a n t a n t a n t a n t a n t a n t a n t a n t
a n t a n t a n t a n t a n t a n t a n t a n t
a n t a n t a n t a n t a n t a n t a n t a n t
a n t a n t a n t a n t a n t a n t a n t a n t
c a n t c o u n t a n t c a n t c o u n t a n t
a n a c c o u n t a n t a n a c c o u n t a n t
a n t e a t e r a n t e a t e r a n t e a t e r
e a t e a t e a t e a t e a t e a t e a t e a t
e a t e a t e a t e a t e a t e a t e a t e a t
a n t e a t e n a n t e a t e n a n t e a t e n
n e c t a r n e c t a r n e c t a r n e c t a r
t r a n c e t r a n c e t r a n c e t r a n c e

*   *   *   *   *   *   *   *   *   *   *   *   *   *

c a n t e a t a n a n t c a n t e a t a n a n t
a n t e a t e r c a n t a n t e a t e r c a n t
n o t a n a n t n o t a n a n t n o t a n a n t

*   *   *   *   *   *   *   *   *   *   *   *   *   *

t r a n c e t r a n c e t r a n c e t r a n c e
o c o n t e n t o c o n t e n t o c o n t e n t
n o c a n t e r n o c a n t e r n o c a n t e r
```

EDWIN MORGAN

Japanese Breakfast

The table of the pool is set.
Each cup quivers by a plate.

Some are filled with tea of sun,
some have pinks of liquor in;

some, thick and white, look upside down
as if put out to dry,

or not to use till morning
pours a thinner cream.

Lying out lopsided,
all the plates are green.

Immaculate as in Japan
the food is only dew,

but fountain-flounce, the table cloth,
shows a rainbow stain.

Some black-nosed goldfish passing through
on their way to shade

nudge the rocking saucers.
A wet ceramic toad,

descending stairs of moss
to breakfast on an insect,

upsets the level table top
but leaves the cups intact.

MAY SWENSON

Lines Written for Gene Kelly to Dance To

Spring is when the grass turns green and glad.
Spring is when the new grass comes up and says, "Hey, hey!
  Hey, hey!"
Be dizzy now and turn your head upside down and see how
  the world looks upside down.
Be dizzy now and turn a cartwheel, and see the good earth
  through a cartwheel.

Tell your feet the alphabet.
Tell your feet the multiplication table.
Tell your feet where to go, and watch 'em go and come back.

Can you dance a question mark?
Can you dance an exclamation point?
Can you dance a couple of commas?
And bring it to a finish with a period?

Can you dance like the wind is pushing you?
Can you dance like you are pushing the wind?
Can you dance with slow wooden heels
  and then change to bright and singing silver heels?
Such nice feet, such good feet.

So long as grass grows and rivers run
Silver lakes like blue porcelain plates
Silver snakes of winding rivers.
You can see 'em on a map.

Why we got geography?
Because we go from place to place. Because the earth used to be flat
  and had four corners, and you could jump off from any of the
  corners.
But now the earth is not flat any more. Now it is round all over.
  Now it is a globe, a ball, round all over, and we would all fall off
  it and tumble away into space if it wasn't for the magnetic poles.
  And when you dance it is the North Pole or the South Pole pulling
  on your feet like magnets to keep your feet on the earth.
And that's why we got geography.
And it's nice to have it that way.

Why does duh Mississippi River wind and wind?
Why, dat's easy. She wind so she git where she wanna go.
Mississippi, Rappahannock, Punxatawney. Spell out their names
with your heels.

Where duh towns uh Punxatawney and Mauk Chunk? Why, yeanh
day's bof in Pennsylvan-ee-eye-ay.
And dat's why we got geography.

Left foot, tweedle-dum — right foot tweedle-dee, here they go.

When Yankee Doodle come to town, wot wuz he a-ridin' on?

A buffalo? A elephant? A horse?
No, no, no, no. A pony it wuz, a pony.
That's right —
Giddi-ap, Giddi-ap, Giddi-ap, Giddi-ap.
Whoa! Whoa!

CARL SANDBURG

Jazz Fantasia

Drum on your drums, batter on your banjoes,
sob on the long cool winding saxophones.
Go to it, O jazzmen.

Sling your knuckles on the bottoms of the happy
tin pans, let your trombones ooze, and go husha-
husha-hush with the slippery sand-paper.

Moan like an autumn wind high in the lonesome treetops,
   moan soft like
you wanted somebody terrible, cry like a racing car slipping
   away from a
motorcycle cop, bang-bang! you jazzmen, bang altogether
   drums, traps,
banjoes, horns, tin cans — make two people fight on the top
   of a stairway
and scratch each other's eyes in a clinch tumbling down the
   stairs.

Can the rough stuff . . . now a Mississippi steamboat pushes
   up the night
river with a hoo-hoo-hoo-oo . . . and the green lanterns calling
   to the high
soft stars . . . a red moon rides on the humps of the low river
   hills . . .
go to it, O jazzmen.

CARL SANDBURG

American Gothic

TO SATCH

Sometimes I feel like I will *never* stop
Just go on forever
'Til one fine mornin'
I'm gonna reach up and grab me a handfulla stars
Swing out my long lean leg
And whip three hot strikes burnin' down the heavens
And look over at God and say
How about that!

94   SAMUEL ALLEN (PAUL VESEY)

French Persian Cats Having a Ball

chat
shah   shah
        chat
             chat   shah   cha   ha
             shah   chat   cha   ha
      shah
      chat
cha
cha

                  ha
                 chat
                 chat
             chatshahchat
         chachacha   chachacha
            shahchatshah
                shah
                shah
                 ha
cha
cha
chatcha
    cha
    shahcha
        cha
        chatcha
           cha
           shahcha
              cha
              cha

                        sh ch
                        aha
                        ch sh

EDWIN MORGAN

A Christmas Tree

Star,
If you are
A love compassionate,
You will walk with us this year.
We face a glacial distance, who are here
Huddl'd
At your feet.

WILLIAM BURFORD

The Snow Man

One must have a mind of winter
To regard the frost and the boughs
Of the pine-trees crusted with snow;

And have been cold a long time
To behold the junipers shagged with ice,
The spruces rough in the distant glitter

Of the January sun; and not to think
Of any misery in the sound of the wind,
In the sound of a few leaves,

Which is the sound of the land
Full of the same wind
That is blowing in the same bare place

For the listener, who listens in the snow,
And, nothing himself, beholds
Nothing that is not there and the nothing that is.

WALLACE STEVENS

Sayings from the Northern Ice

It is people at the edge who say
things at the edge: winter is toward knowing.

    Sled runners before they meet have long talk apart.
    There is a pup in every litter the wolves will have.
    A knife that falls points at an enemy.
    Rocks in the wind know their place: down low.
    Over your shoulder is God; the dying deer sees him.

At the mouth of the long sack we fall in forever
storms brighten the spikes of the stars.

    Wind that buried bear skulls north of here
    and beats moth wings for help outside the door
    is bringing bear skull wisdom, but do not ask the skull
    too large a question till summer.
    Something too dark was held in that strong bone.

Better to end with a lucky saying:

    Sled runners cannot decide to join or to part.
    When they decide, it is a bad day.

WILLIAM STAFFORD

How To Paint a Perfect Christmas

Above, you paint the sky
delicate as maidenhair.
Below, pour a little darkness
heated to room temperature
or slightly more.

With a cat's claw in the dark
scratch out a little tree,
the finest tree in the world,
finer than any forester
could ever imagine.

And the tree itself
will light up
and the whole picture purr
with green joy,
with purple hope.

Right. But now you must
put under the tree
the
real big thing,
the thing you most want in the world;
the thing pop-singers
call happiness.

It's easy enough for a cat,
a cat will put a mouse there,
Colonel Blimp will line up
the largest jet-propelled halberd
which shoots and bangs and salutes,
a sparrow will gather
a few stalks for its nest,
mister junior clerk will submit
a stuffed file tied with red tape,
a butterfly will put there
a new rubber peacock's eye,
but what will *you* put there?

You think and think
till the day grows grey,
till the river almost runs out,
till even the bulbs begin to yawn,
you think

and finally

there in the darkness you blot out
a hazy white spot,
a bit like a florin,
a bit like a ship,
a bit like a Moon,
a bit like the beautiful face
of someone (who?) else,

a hazy white spot,
perhaps more like emptiness,
like the negation of something,
like non-pain,
like non-fear,
like non-worry,

a hazy white spot,
and you go to bed
and say to yourself,
yes, now I know how to do it,
yes, now I know,
yes,
next time
I shall paint
the most perfect Christmas
that ever was.

MIROSLAV HOLUB Translated from the Czech by Ian Milner and George Theiner

Wings

We have
a microscopic anatomy
of the whale
this
gives
Man
assurance

WILLIAM CARLOS WILLIAMS

We have
a map of the universe
for microbes,
we have
a map of a microbe
for the universe.

We have
a Grand Master of chess
made of electronic circuits.

But above all
we have
the ability
to sort peas,
to cup water in our hands,
to seek
the right screw
under the sofa
for hours.

This
gives us
wings.

MIROSLAV HOLUB Translated from the Czech by George Theiner

Ice-Fishing

Not thinking other than how the hand works
I wait until dark here on the cold
world rind, ice-curved over simplest rock
where the tugged river flows over hidden
springs too insidious to be quite forgotten.

When the night comes I plunge my hand
where the string of fish know their share
of the minimum. Then, bringing back my hand
is a great sunburst event; and slow
home with me over unmarked snow

In the wild flipping warmth of won-back thought
my boots, my hat, my body go.

WILLIAM STAFFORD

Lament

Because I have no time
To set my ladder up, and climb
Out of the dung and straw,
Green poems laid in a dark store
Shrivel and grow soft
Like unturned apples in a loft.

JON STALLWORTHY

An Empty Threat

I stay;
But it isn't as if
There wasn't always Hudson's Bay
And the fur trade,
A small skiff
And a paddle blade.

I can just see my tent pegged,
And me on the floor,
Crosslegged,
And a trapper looking in at the door
With furs to sell.

His name's Joe,
Alias John,
And between what he doesn't know
And won't tell
About where Henry Hudson's gone,
I can't say he's much help;
But we get on.

The sea yelp
On an ice cake.
It's not men by some mistake?

No,
There's not a soul
For a wind-break
Between me and the North Pole —

Except always John-Joe,
My French Indian Esquimaux,
And he's off setting traps,
In one himself perhaps.

Give a head shake
Over so much bay
Thrown away
In snow and mist
That doesn't exist,

I was going to say,
For God, man or beast's sake,
Yet does perhaps for all three.

Don't ask Joe
What it is to him.
It's sometimes dim
What it is to me,
Unless it be
It's the old captain's dark fate
Who failed to find or force a strait
In its two-thousand-mile coast;
And his crew left him where he failed,
And nothing came of all he sailed.

It's to say, "You and I"
To such a ghost,
"You and I
Off here
With the dead race of the Great Auk!"
And, "Better defeat almost,
If seen clear,
Than life's victories of doubt
That need endless talk talk
To make them out."

ROBERT FROST

Philosopher

He scowled at the barometer: "Will it rain?"
None heard, with all that pattering on the pane.

JOHN FREDERICK NIMS

Thistles

Against the rubber tongues of cows and the hoeing hands of men
Thistles spike the summer air
Or crackle open under a blue-black pressure.

Every one a revengeful burst
Of resurrection, a grasped fistful
Of splintered weapons and Icelandic frost thrust up

From the underground stain of a decayed Viking.
They are like pale hair and the gutturals of dialects.
Every one manages a plume of blood.

Then they grow grey, like men.
Mown down, it is a feud. Their sons appear,
Stiff with weapons, fighting back over the same ground.

TED HUGHES

Names

A skein of suns, the uncut stones of night,
Calm planets rising, violet, golden, red —
Bear names evolved from man's enormous head:
Of gods who govern battle, rivers, flight,
And goddesses of science and delight;
Arranged in the mortal shapes of those who bled
To found a dynasty or in great dread
Slept with their destiny, full-breasted, white.
But long before stout Venus, clanking Mars,
What appellations had the eternal stars?
When, cheek by jowl with burial pits, rank dens
Lay open to the dark, and dwarfish men
Stared under huge brow-ridges, wits awry,
What fearful monsters slouched about the sky?

ROY FULLER

The Trap

The first night that the monster lurched
Out of the forest on all fours,
He saw its shadow in his dream
Circle the house, as though it searched
For one it loved or hated. Claws
On gravel and a rabbit's scream
Ripped the fabric of his dream.

Waking between dark and dawn
And sodden sheets, his reason quelled
The shadow and the nightmare sound.
The second night it crossed the lawn
A brute voice in the darkness yelled.
He struggled up, woke raving, found
His wall-flowers trampled to the ground.

When rook wings beckoned the shadows back
He took his rifle down, and stood
All night against the leaded glass.
The moon ticked round. He saw the black
Elm-skeletons in the doomsday wood,
The sailing and the failing stars
And red coals dropping between bars.

The third night such a putrid breath
Fouled, flared his nostrils, that he turned,
Turned, but could not lift, his head.
A coverlet as thick as death
Oppressed him: he crawled out: discerned
Across the door his watchdog, dead.
"Build a trap," the neighbors said.

All that day he built his trap
With metal jaws and a spring as thick
As the neck of a man. One touch
Triggered the hanging teeth: jump, snap,
And lightning guillotined the stick
Thrust in its throat. With gun and torch
He set his engine in the porch.

The fourth night in their beds appalled
His neighbors heard the hunting roar
Mount, mount to an exultant shriek.
At daybreak timidly they called
His name, climbed through the splintered door,
And found him sprawling in the wreck,
Naked, with a severed neck.

JON STALLWORTHY

Two Wise Generals

"Not as Black Douglas, bannered, trumpeted,
Who hacked for the casked heart flung to the enemy,
Letting the whole air flow breakneck with blood
Till he fell astride that handful, you and I

Come, two timid and ageing generals
To parley, and to divide the territory
Upon a map, and get honour, and by
This satisfaction part with regiments whole."

They entered the lit tent, in no hurry to grab.
Apart in darkness twinkled their armies
Like two safe towns. Thus they drank, joked, waxed wise —
So heavily medalled never need fear stab.

The treaty sealed, lands allotted (and a good third
Stuffed down their tunic fronts' private estate)
They left the empty bottle. The tent-lamp out,
They lurched away in the knee-high mist, hearing the first bird,

Towards separate camps.
                        Now, one a late dew-moth
Eyes, as he sways, among the still tents. The other roars "Guard!"
As a fox ducks from the silent parapet. Both
Have found their sleeping armies massacred.

TED HUGHES

The Performance

The last time I saw Donald Armstrong
He was staggering oddly off into the sun,
Going down, of the Philippine Islands.
I let my shovel fall, and put that hand
Above my eyes, and moved some way to one side
That his body might pass through the sun,

And I saw how well he was not
Standing there on his hands,
On his spindle-shanked forearms balanced,
Unbalanced, with his big feet looming and waving
In the great, untrustworthy air
He flew in each night, when it darkened.

Dust fanned in scraped puffs from the earth
Between his arms, and blood turned his face inside out,
To demonstrate its suppleness
Of veins, as he perfected his role.
Next day, he toppled his head off
On an island beach to the south,

And the enemy's two-handed sword
Did not fall from anyone's hands
At that miraculous sight,
As the head rolled over upon
Its wide-eyed face, and fell
Into the inadequate grave

He had dug for himself, under pressure.
Yet I put my flat hand to my eyebrows
Months later, to see him again
In the sun, when I learned how he died,
And imagined him, there,
Come, judged, before his small captors,

Doing all his lean tricks to amaze them —
The back somersault, the kip-up —
And at last, the stand on his hands,
Perfect, with his feet together,
His head down, evenly breathing,
As the sun poured up from the sea

And the headsman broke down
In a blaze of tears, in that light
Of the thin, long human frame
Upside down in its own strange joy,
And, if some other one had not told him,
Would have cut off the feet

Instead of the head,
And if Armstrong had not presently risen
In kingly, round-shouldered attendance,
And then knelt down in himself
Beside his hacked, glittering grave, having done
All things in this life that he could.

JAMES DICKEY

The Death of a Soldier

Life contracts and death is expected,
As in a season of autumn.
The soldier falls.

He does not become a three-days personage,
Imposing his separation.
Calling for pomp.

Death is absolute and without memorial,
As in a season of autumn,
When the wind stops,

When the wind stops and, over the heavens.
The clouds go, nevertheless,
In their direction.

WALLACE STEVENS

Ten Days Leave

He steps down from the dark train, blinking; stares
At trees like miracles. He will play games
With boys or sit up all night touching chairs.
Talking with friends, he can recall their names.

Noon burns against his eyelids, but he lies
Hunched in his blankets; he is half awake
But still lacks nerve to open up his eyes;
Supposing it were just his old mistake?

But no; it seems just like it seemed. His folks
Pursue their lives like toy trains on a track.
He can foresee each of his father's jokes
Like words in some old movie that's come back.

He is like days when you've gone some place new
To deal with certain strangers, though you never
Escape the sense in everything you do,
"We've done this all once. Have I been here, ever?"

But no; he thinks it must recall some old film, lit
By lives you want to touch; as if he'd slept
And must have dreamed this setting, peopled it,
And wakened out of it. But someone's kept

His dream asleep here like a small homestead
Preserved long past its time in memory
Of some great man who lived here and is dead.
They have restored his landscape faithfully:

The hills, the little houses, the costumes:
How real it seems! But he comes, wide awake,
A tourist whispering through the priceless rooms
Who must not touch things or his hand might break

Their sleep and black them out. He wonders when
He'll grow into his sleep so sound again.

W. D. SNODGRASS

Knowlt Hoheimer

I was the first fruits of the battle of Missionary Ridge.
When I felt the bullet enter my heart
I wished I had staid at home and gone to jail
For stealing the hogs of Curl Trenary,
Instead of running away and joining the army.
Rather a thousand times the county jail
Than to lie under this marble figure with wings,
And this granite pedestal
Bearing the words, *"Pro Patria."*
What do they mean, anyway?

EDGAR LEE MASTERS

Contrary Theses (I)

Now grapes are plush upon the vines.
A soldier walks before my door.

The hives are heavy with the combs.
Before, before, before my door.

And seraphs cluster on the domes,
And saints are brilliant in fresh cloaks.

Before, before, before my door.
The shadows lessen on the walls.

The bareness of the house returns.
An acid sunlight fills the halls.

Before, before. Blood smears the oaks.
A soldier stalks before my door.

WALLACE STEVENS

Lull
(November, 1939)

The winds of hatred blow
Cold, cold across the flesh
And chill the anxious heart;
Intricate phobias grow
From each malignant wish
To spoil collective life.
Now each man stands apart.

We watch opinion drift,
Think of our separate skins.
On well-upholstered bums
The generals cough and shift
Playing with painted pins.
The arbitrators wait;
The newsmen suck their thumbs.
The mind is quick to turn
Away from simple faith
To the cant and fury of
Fools who will never learn;
Reason embraces death,
While out of frightened eyes
Still stares the wish to love.

THEODORE ROETHKE

What Were They Like?

1   Did the people of Viet Nam
    use lanterns of stone?
2   Did they hold ceremonies
    to reverence the opening of buds?
3   Were they inclined to quiet laughter?
4   Did they use bone and ivory,
    jade and silver, for ornament?
5   Had they an epic poem?
6   Did they distinguish between speech and singing?

1   Sir, their light hearts turned to stone.
It is not remembered whether in gardens
stone lanterns illumined pleasant ways.

2   Perhaps they gathered once to delight in blossom,
but after the children were killed
there were no more buds.

3   Sir, laughter is bitter to the burned mouth.

4   A dream ago, perhaps. Ornament is for joy.
All the bones were charred.

5   It is not remembered. Remember,
most were peasants; their life
was in rice and bamboo.
When peaceful clouds were reflected in the paddies
and the water buffalo stepped surely along terraces,
maybe fathers told their sons old tales.
When bombs smashed those mirrors
there was time only to scream.

6   There is an echo yet
of their speech which was like a song.
It was reported their singing resembled
the flight of moths in moonlight.
Who can say? It is silent now.

DENISE LEVERTOV

There Will Come Soft Rains
War Time

There will come soft rains and the smell of the ground,
And swallows circling with their shimmering sound;

And frogs in the pools singing at night,
And wild plum-trees in tremulous white.

Robins will wear their feathery fire
Whistling their whims on a low fence-wire;

And not one will know of the war, not one
Will care at last when it is done.

Not one would mind, neither bird nor tree,
If mankind perished utterly;

And Spring herself, when she woke at dawn
Would scarcely know that we were gone.

SARA TEASDALE

F for Francis

F for Francis,
I for Jancis,
N for Nickley Boney,
I for John the Waterman, and
S for Signey Coney.

TRADITIONAL

List of Illustrations

(*Acknowledgements continued*)

Poems and Plays by T. S. Eliot. Copyright 1950 by T. S. Eliot, 1952 by Harcourt, Brace and Company, Inc. For "Buyers and Sellers," "City Number," "Dreaming Fool," "Fame If Not Fortune," "Is Wisdom a Lot of Language?" and "Lines Written for Gene Kelly to Dance To," all from *Complete Poems of Carl Sandburg*. Copyright 1950 by Carl Sandburg. For Extracts from "The People, Yes" from *The Sandburg Range*, copyright 1957 by Carl Sandburg. For "Jazz Fantasia" and "Soup" from *Smoke and Steel* by Carl Sandburg. Copyright © 1920 by Harcourt, Brace & World, Inc. Copyright © 1950 by Carl Sandburg. All reprinted by permission by Harcourt, Brace & World, Inc.

Harper & Row, Publishers, Inc.: For "Thistles" from *Wodwo* by Ted Hughes. Copyright © 1961 by Ted Hughes. For "Two Wise Generals" from *The Hawk in the Rain* by Ted Hughes. Copyright 1957 by Ted Hughes. For "Ice-Fishing" and "Vacation" from *The Rescued Year* by William E. Stafford, copyright © 1960 by William E. Stafford. For "Ex-Basketball Player" from *The Carpentered Hen and Other Tame Creatures* by John Updike. Copyright © 1957 by John Updike. All reprinted by permission of Harper & Row, Publishers.

David Higham Associates, Ltd.: For "The Ballad of the Bread Man" by Charles Causley from *Modern Folk Ballads*.

Holt, Rinehart and Winston, Inc.: For "An Empty Threat" and "Fire and Ice" from *Complete Poems of Robert Frost*. Copyright 1916, 1923, 1930, 1939 by Holt, Rinehart and Winston, Inc. Copyright 1936, 1944, 1951, © 1958 by Robert Frost. Copyright © 1964, 1967 by Lesley Frost Ballantine. For "To an Athlete Dying Young" from "A Shropshire Lad"—Authorized Edition—from *The Collected Poems of A. E. Housman*. Copyright 1939, 1940, © 1959 by Holt, Rinehart and Winston, Inc. Copyright © 1967, 1968 by Robert E. Symons. All reprinted by permission of Holt, Rinehart and Winston, Inc.

Indiana University Press: For "Africa's Plea" by Roland Tombekai Dempster from *Poems from Black Africa*, edited by Langston Hughes. Published by Indiana University Press.

Margot Johnson Agency: For "Mousemeal" from *New and Selected Poems* by Howard Nemerov. Copyright 1960 by The University of Chicago Press.

Alfred A. Knopf, Inc.: For "Epitaph on a Tyrant" from *Shorter Collected Poems* by W. H. Auden. Copyright 1944 by W. H. Auden. For "I, Too, Sing America" from *Selected Poems* by Langston Hughes. Copyright 1951, 1959 by Langston Hughes. For "Ten Days Leave," copyright © 1956 by W. D. Snodgrass. Reprinted from *Heart's Needle*, by W. D. Snodgrass. Reprinted by permision of Alfred A. Knopf, Inc. For "Parting, Without a Sequel" from *Selected Poems* by John Crowe Ransom. Copyright 1962, 1963 by Alfred A. Knopf, Inc. For "Contrary Theses (I)," "The Death of a Soldier," and "The Snow Man" from *The Collected Poems of Wallace Stevens*. Copyright 1954 by Wallace Stevens. All reprinted by permission of Alfred A. Knopf, Inc.

Little, Brown and Company: For "Cat-Faith," copyright © 1959 by Alastair Reid, and "Pigeons," copyright 1954 by Alastair Reid; originally appeared in *The New Yorker;* from *Oddments, Inklings, Omens, Moments* by Alastair Reid. Reprinted by permission of Atlantic, Little, Brown and Company.

Liveright Publishing Corporation: For "When You're Away" by Samuel Hoffenstein from *A Treasury of Humorous Verse*.

The Macmillan Company: For "American Gothic" by Samuel Allen (Paul Vesey) from *I Am the Darker Brother*. Copyright © 1968, The Macmillan Company. For "Knowlt Hoheimer" from *Spoon River Anthology* by Edgar Lee Masters. Copyright © 1962 by The Crowell-Collier Publishing Company. For "There Will Come Soft Rains" from *Collected Poems* by Sara Teasdale. Copyright 1920 by The

Index of Titles and Poets

124